FEEDING TUBE RECIPE FOR OPTIMUM HEALTH

BY
NANCY ADDISON

ORGANIC HEALTHY LIFESTYLE PUBLISHING
2017

Feeding Tube Recipe for Optimum Health

ISBN-10: 0-9961085-8-0
ISBN-13: 978-0-9961085-8-4

Nancy Alisa Gibbons Addison www.OrganicHealthyLife.com

Limits of Liability and Disclaimer of Warranty:
The author and publisher are not liable for misuse of this material. This book is strictly for informational and educational purposes. Nancy Addison offers information and opinions, not a substitute for professional medical prevention, diagnosis, or treatment. Please consult with your physician, pharmacist, or healthcare provider before taking any home remedies or supplements, or following any treatment suggested by Nancy Addison or by anyone listed in the books, articles, or other information contained here. Only your healthcare provider, personal physician, or pharmacist can provide you with advice on what is safe and effective for your unique needs or diagnose your particular medical history.

Warning & Disclaimer:
The purpose of this book is to educate and entertain. The author and publisher do not guarantee that anyone following these techniques, suggestions, tips, ideas, or strategies will become successful. The author and publisher shall have neither liability nor responsibility to anyone with respect to any loss or damage caused, or alleged to be caused, directly or indirectly by the information contained in this book.

About the Author

Nancy Addison is a certified health counselor accredited by both Columbia University and the Institute of Integrative Nutrition. She holds a Certificate of Plant-Based Nutrition from Cornell University and the T. Colin Campbell Foundation, and is a board-certified health practitioner with the American Association of Drugless Practitioners.

Nancy studied with Natalia Rose and the Rose Program in Detoxification, and she is a certified raw food chef, instructor, and teacher with Alissa Cohen. Nancy is certified in Basic Intensive in Health—Supportive Cooking from the Natural Gourmet Institute for Food & Health in New York. She studied at Le Cordon Bleu culinary school in London, England, and at the Mediterranean Cooking School in Syros, Greece with the Australasian College of Health Science. Nancy also studied Chinese Gastronomy in London, England.

Nancy has studied Thai Cooking in Thailand, Khmer Cooking in Cambodia, and Malay Cooking in South Africa. She also studied conscious farming (organic gardening) at the Tree of Life Rejuvenation Center with John M. Phillips of the Living Earth Training Center. Nancy is a Psychosomatic Therapy Certified Practitioner with the Australasian Institute of Body-Mind Analysis and Psychosomatic Therapy. She is a certified personal trainer with American Sports and Fitness Association, and a member of the American Nutritionist Association.

Nancy is the author of the #1 bestseller *Raising Healthy Children* (winner of the Mom's Choice Award for Excellence), the second edition of the best-selling *How to Be a Healthy Vegetarian* (finalist in two categories of the Indie Book Awards, finalist in the International Book Awards and North Texas Book Festival), *Diabetes and Your Diet* (#1 best-seller and a finalist in the North Texas Book Festival) and *Lose Weight, Get Healthy & Never Have to Be on a Diet Again*. She co-authored *Alive and Cooking: An Easy Guide to Health for You and Your Parents*. Nancy's five books have been endorsed by world-renowned doctors.

Nancy is featured in the documentary *Eating You Alive*, along with Dr. T. Colin Campbell, Dr. Dean Ornish, and Dr. Caldwell B. Esselstyn, Jr.

Nancy hosts the radio show *Organic Healthy Lifestyle,* as featured on **I Heart Radio** and W4CY Radio.

Nancy was awarded *Woman of the Year* in 2013 by the National Association of Professional Women. Nancy was also the personal chef and nutrition consultant to Larry Hagman (known as JR Ewing in the TV show *Dallas*).

She is a member of the National Speakers Association and the Global Speakers Federation. Nancy holds a Bachelor of Arts degree from Hollins

College (now University) in Roanoke, Virginia, and she holds a lifelong Texas teaching certificate for all grade levels. She is a certified wildlife rehabilitator and a magazine columnist. Nancy also served as secretary of the Earth Society, an affiliate of the United Nations.

OrganicHealthyLife.com

Contents

1
Introduction

The body requires proper nutrition to stay healthy and strong. If you're unable to eat and it's hard to swallow food, you may need a feeding tube, which is called percutaneous endoscopic gastrostomy—or PEG, for short. The tube is surgically inserted into your stomach to provide food, liquids, and/or medicines.

Even with a feeding tube, you can get the essential nutrients you need for healing, creating a strong immune system, and maintaining body weight. A healthy diet includes proteins, fats, carbohydrates and optimum hydration. They are all important components and work together like a symphony in the body.

Getting a feeding tube means you need to learn some new skills, including how to use and care for the tube.

Eight Tips for Tube Feeding.

1. Always wash your hands before you handle the tube or the food you combine for the formula. Also make certain your food is clean.

2. When you are ready to put the food into the tube, the food should be room temperature. Never use cold food for the feeding. Cold food will prevent your body from digesting properly.

3. If you are using a feeding syringe, first connect the syringe to the tube, and put the formula into the syringe. Then, hold the syringe up high so the formula flows into the tube. If it gets stuck, gently use the plunger on the syringe to carefully push any remaining formula into the tube.

4. If using a gravity bag, connect the bag to the tube and add the formula to the bag. Then hang the bag on a hook about 18 inches above the stomach. With a bag, it can take a few hours for the formula to completely flow through the tube.

5. For the person getting the tube feeding, they should be sitting up, with their head up during the feeding. If the person getting the feeding starts to feel sick, then have the person administering the feeding slow it down. Talk with your doctor if the person getting the feeding has diarrhea, constipation, or vomiting.

6. When you are finished with the feeding, clean the tube and all its components. Flush the tube and all its components with clean, warm water immediately before and after administering a feeding. You can use a syringe to push water through the tube. Every day, clean the end (the opening) of the tube with an antiseptic wipe. I use food-grade hydrogen peroxide (35% solution).

7. When finished with a feeding, clamp the tube connected to the stomach, and put the clamp close to the body so food and liquids don't run down the tube. To keep the skin around the tube clean, wash it with a mild soap. I use one with an antibacterial essential oil in it, such as lemon. If the skin is getting dry, put a little pure organic coconut oil on it.

8. If your tube gets blocked when doing a feeding, the formula may be too thick. You can add some liquid to it and run it through a sieve to thin it down. Just remember to always flush out the tube with warm water immediately following a feeding. If the tube won't clear out, you may need to get another one. Avoid using any kind of wire or device to clear it, because that might puncture the tube.

Call your health care provider if you have any problems or questions. Adapting to this process may take a little time and patience, but before you know it, you will get accustomed to doing it easily and accurately. As you start on this program, focus and concentrate on what you are doing and be faithful in the fundamentals of keeping the equipment clean. Just remember that obtaining optimum nutrition can be one of the most important parts of maximum health and healing for a radiantly healthy life.

2
Tube Feeding

Tube feeding is much more prevalent than most of us imagine. And for a person faced with the inability to swallow, it can be a life-or-death situation.

As a certified wildlife rehabilitator, I was a specialist in tube feeding for animals before I knew I would need to be a specialist in tube feeding for people, too. If animals are incapacitated or unable to eat on their own, they can die of starvation. To feed them precise amounts of nutrition, I use a syringe and a long tube. I put the tube very gently down the animal's throat.

For humans, a feeding tube is a medical device used to provide nutrition to patients who cannot obtain nutrition by mouth, since their throat may have some problems which make it impossible for them to swallow. Needing to be fed by a tube is called gavage, enteral feeding, or tube feeding. The tube is connected to the stomach, so you can insert food directly into the stomach without the person having to chew or swallow. The tube may be temporary for the treatment of acute conditions, or it could be permanent for some people with chronic disabilities.

When I started working as a nutritionist and chef for Larry Hagman (an actor known for his part as J. R. Ewing in the TV show *Dallas*), he had throat cancer and diabetes. Larry had a liver transplant 16 years before, and the medications he took to help his body accept the liver had also given him diabetes. A medical doctor I work with helped me analyze Larry's medications, and he told me that three of those medications had been proven to cause cancer.

Larry wanted to change his diet to help his body heal. I started him on very alkaline, mostly vegan, raw foods combined with some cooked food.

For a time, Larry had so much trouble swallowing that he needed tube feeding. He had the surgery at the hospital and came home with cans of liquid the doctors made him purchase for the tube feeding. He asked what I thought of them.

The ingredients label showed high-fructose corn syrup (which is a very harmful ingredient for a person with diabetes or cancer), various artificial ingredients, and a long list of chemicals. The manufacturers only seemed to be concerned about how many calories there were, and not the quality of the food. This approach, in my opinion, is not beneficial nutrition for someone trying to heal or have optimum health.

While glucose is designed to be used by your body for energy, high-fructose sugar breaks down into a variety of toxins that can destroy a person's health. I wanted to avoid any kind of artificial types of sugar or high-fructose sweetener. Consumption of high-fructose sugar:

- Elevates uric acid, which can cause inflammation, hypertension, kidney disease, and fatty liver.

- Leads to insulin resistance, a factor in Type 2 diabetes, heart diseases, and many cancers.
- Tricks your body into gaining weight. Fructose doesn't appropriately stimulate insulin, which, as a result, fails to suppress ghrelin ("hunger hormone") and to stimulate leptin ("satiety hormone").
- Rapidly leads to metabolic syndrome, with weight gain as the result. It can also decrease HDL, increase LDL, elevate triglycerides, elevate blood sugar, and cause high blood pressure. Metabolizes like ethanol, causing toxic effects like non-alcoholic fatty liver diseases (NAFLD).[1]

These findings are supported by research by Dr. Richard Johnson, author of *The Fat Switch*. In a 10-week study, Dr. Johnson had 16 volunteers go on a controlled diet which included high levels of fructose. They produced new fat cells around their hearts, livers, and digestive organs. They also showed signs of abnormalities linked to diabetes and heart disease.

Another group of volunteers on the same diet, but with glucose sugar replacing fructose, did not have these problems. The study showed that fructose in any form—including high-fructose corn syrup (HFCS) and crystalline fructose—is very harmful to health.

---

[1] Mercola, Joseph. "The Deliberate Lies They Tell About Diabetes". http://www.mercola.com/diabetes.aspx [Summarizing material from Dr. Richard Johnson's *The Fat Switch*.]

I said to Larry, "I think we can do better." I wanted him to have the most intense nutrition, with high alkalinity, and combined with enough fat and calories to provide the energy and vitality, but also to maintain weight.

With diabetes, cancer, and healing in mind, I created some recipes for maximum nutrition. Someone with a feeding tube doesn't taste what comes through the tube, so there is the opportunity to create a nutrient-dense mixture without regard to flavor. I recommend a vegetarian mixture, mostly raw, that has no sugar or is extremely low in sugar. Avoid using anything with high fructose corn syrup in it.

Over the years, many people have asked me for recipes for feeding tubes. So, I am sharing this recipe and the nutrition information with you. Please use it as a guide, expand on it, and adjust it to the foods you have available to you. May you and your loved ones find optimum nutrition, health, and well-being.

3
Nancy's Tube Feeding Recipe

I recommend using all non-GMO, organic, fresh, vine or tree-ripened ingredients. You can mix some high quality, non-chlorinated water with this if it is too thick. You can expand on this recipe, and I'll list a few alternatives you can use for variety.

1 serving, 698 calories. (If you feel you need more calories, add more coconut oil to the mix.)

Ingredients:
1 avocado = 234 calories
2 T. coconut oil = 234 calories (117 per T.)
2 T. cold-pressed hemp or flax seed oil = 112 calories
1 cucumber (juiced and used within 20 minutes) = 16 calories
4–6 stems of celery (juiced and used within 20 minutes) = 30 calories
2 ounces fresh, wheat grass juice = 10 calories
1 lemon or lime juiced with rind = 2 calories
3 tsp. spirulina = 30 calories
1 tsp. chlorella = 10 calories
1-2 capsule of digestive enzymes (open the capsule and empty the contents into the mix)
¼ cup wild blueberries = 20 calories

¼ tsp. unrefined, mineral rich sea salt (example: Himalayan or Bolivian Rose salt.)

At least once a day, add the following:

2 whole-food multivitamins in liquid or capsule form (emptied from the capsule)

I recommend only using vitamins made of whole, real food. Avoid vitamins made from synthetic ingredients.[2] I use Garden of Life brand vitamins, because they are made with whole, organic, raw, gluten-free food.

1–2 tsp. probiotics (cold, from the refrigerated section of the grocery store. I used one made from organic coconut, but Garden of Life has a new one made in a capsule form that can be used as well.)

1 or 2 eggs (fresh, organic, humanely and pastured-raised) including the yolk and white. There are about 55 calories in a medium egg.

A Note about Eggs: Add eggs to the morning feeding, because there are "significant benefits to consuming more protein at breakfast, such as stimulation of muscle protein synthesis and long-lasting satiety."[3] New research from *Edelman Public Relations* shows the affordable, high-quality protein in eggs contributes to power, strength, and sustained energy. For more information on eggs, see "Protein" in the chapter, *Additional Nutrient Information.*

---

[2] Hendler, SS, & Rorvik, D. (2008). *PDR for Nutritional Supplements.* (2008). Montvale, NJ: Physicians' Desk Reference Inc.

Shils ME, Olson JA, Shike M. (1999). *Modern Nutrition in Health and Disease,* 9th ed. Williams & Wilkins: Balt.

Thiel, R. (2000). "Natural vitamins may be superior to synthetic ones." *Med Hypo,* 55(6): 461-469.

[3] EurekaAlert! (February 17, 2009).

Optional Additions:

You can add any of the following foods and supplements to the mixture for super health benefits and variety.

½ dropper of fulvic acid

½ tsp. chaga mushroom powder or extract

½ tsp. reishi mushroom powder or extract

½ tsp. macuna root powder

½–1 cup of micro greens

1 small red beet freshly juiced.

1 -2 T. protein powder (Garden of Life or Sun Warrior are both good choices.)

½ tsp. Ceylon cinnamon

¼ tsp. turmeric (Turmeric is more effective when combined with a tiny bit of fat and black pepper.)

1 capsule of iodoral emptied into the mixture. Iodoral is an iodine and iodide combination created by Dr. David Brownstein. (See the following page.) Order Iodoral from his website, www.drbrownstein.com.

Directions:

1. Blend ingredients in a blender.
2. Pour the mix through a sieve to remove the larger fibers.
3. Place the strained mix into the syringe, and it's ready to administer.

Dr. David Brownstein is one of the top thyroid experts in the world. He feels iodine is the most misunderstood nutrient. He feels it is impossible to achieve your optimal health when you have an iodine deficiency. His books on iodine and the thyroid are excellent resources. His books provide information on how iodine therapy can help:

- ADHD
- Autism
- Breast, Thyroid, Ovarian, and Uterine Cancer
- Detoxification
- Fatigue
- Fibrocystic Breasts
- Graves' Disease
- Hashimoto's Disease
- Hypothyroidism
- Weak Immune Systems

4
Twelve High-Calorie, Nutrient-Dense Whole Foods for Tube Feeding

1. Cucumbers are high in natural electrolytes and nutrients, and they are very hydrating. They are high in iron as well as vitamin C, which makes the iron much more absorbable to the body. Cucumbers are also high in magnesium, panthotheric acid, phosphorus, potassium, riboflavin, thiamin, Vitamin A, and Vitamin B6.

I used them as a liquid base to the food mixture by freshly juicing the cucumber. This thins the mixture and makes it go more smoothly through a feeding tube.

2. Celery is high in natural electrolytes and nutrients, so it is a wonderful way to hydrate the body. Celery is low in saturated fat with no cholesterol. It is high in calcium and magnesium, which means the calcium will be better absorbed by the body.

Other nutrients in celery are: manganese, pantothenic acid, potassium, riboflavin, Vitamins A, B6, and, C. B6 is a very important nutrient that is lacking in many diets. It is available in both cucumber and celery. Celery can also be juiced to use as a liquid base for the other foods, to make a mixture that easily flows through a feeding tube.

3. Avocados have many wonderful qualities, including an insulin-type action. "Insulin is a hormone secreted by your pancreas, and its function is to regulate blood glucose levels. Insulin works like a key to open the door of the cells so glucose—the fuel you get from food—can come inside and be converted into energy."[4]

Researchers have shown that "extracts from Hass avocados kill or stop the growth of pre-cancerous cells that lead to oral cancer."[5] "These studies suggest that individual and a combination of phytochemicals from the avocado fruit may offer an advantageous dietary strategy in cancer prevention," according to a member of the Ohio State University's division of Radiobiology, a Department of Radiology.[6]

4. Flax Seed Oil. Flax seeds are one of the best sources of Omega 3 essential fatty acids. Flax seeds are rich with alpha-Linolenic acid, fiber, and lignans. Lignans are phytoestrogens or plant compounds that have an estrogen-like effect with anti-oxidant properties. These lignans can help stabilize hormone levels. They

[4] Nazor, Nina. "All About Insulin." *People and Diabetes* website. peopleanddiabetes.com/id26.html.
[5] Ohio State University. (September 5, 2007). "Avocados May Help Prevent Oral Cancer, Study Shows." *Science Daily.* http://www.sciencedaily.com/releases/2007/09/070904114442.htm
[6] Ibid.

can also potentially help reduce the risk of developing prostate or breast cancer. The alpha-linolenic acid is anti-inflammatory. It promotes the lowering of the C-Reactive Protein in the blood, which is a biomarker of inflammation.

Essential fatty acids are called essential because our bodies do not make them, and they must be obtained through our diet. Because of their anti-inflammatory properties, Omega 3 fatty acids help with the prevention of many health problems: heart disease, rheumatoid arthritis, macular degeneration, asthma, eczema, other immune dysfunctions, and cancer. Omega 3 fatty acids also help with improving memory and can help improve mood. A deficiency may appear as inflammation, water retention, and high blood pressure.

I like raw, organic, cold-pressed flax seed oil.

1 T. (14 grams) = 110 calories.

5. Hemp oil contains significant amounts of Omega 3 and Omega 6 fatty acids. Hemp oil also contains significant amounts of Vitamin E, which is important for the thyroid gland. Since it is not optimum to have the same exact food every single day, I alternate hemp oil and flax seed oil for the Omega 3 nutrients. One easy thing you can do for your diet is to freshly grind hemp or flax seeds and add them to recipes for an extra benefit of Omega oils, as well as protein and fiber.

6. Wheatgrass is a unique and beneficial food to juice. Dr. Yoshihide Hagiwara, president of the Hagiwara Institute of Health in Japan, advocates the use of grass as food and medicine. Grass is rich in chlorophyll. Chlorophyll is very similar to hemoglobin, a compound in blood that carries oxygen. According to Ann Wigmore's *The Wheatgrass Book*, you benefit from drinking freshly juiced wheatgrass on a regular basis because it:

- Increases red blood-cell count and lowers blood pressure.
- Cleanses the blood, organs, and gastrointestinal tract of debris.
- Stimulates metabolism and the body's enzyme systems by enriching the blood.
- Aids in reducing blood pressure by dilating the blood pathways throughout the body.
- Stimulates the thyroid gland, correcting obesity, indigestion, and a host of other complaints.
- Restores alkalinity to the blood. The juice's abundance of alkaline minerals helps reduce over-acidity in the blood.
- Can be used to relieve many internal pains, and has been used successfully to treat peptic ulcers, ulcerative colitis, constipation, diarrhea, and other complaints of the gastrointestinal tract.
- Is a powerful detoxifier, and liver and blood protector. The enzymes and amino acids found

in wheatgrass can protect us from carcinogens like no other food or medicine.

- Strengthens our cells, detoxifies the liver and bloodstream, and chemically neutralizes environmental pollutants.
- Neutralizes toxic substances such as cadmium, nicotine, strontium, mercury, and polyvinyl chloride.
- Offers the benefits of a liquid oxygen transfusion since the juice contains liquid oxygen. Oxygen is vital to many body processes. It stimulates digestion (the oxidation of food), promotes clearer thinking (the brain utilizes 25% of the body's oxygen supply), and protects the blood against anaerobic bacteria. Cancer cells cannot exist in the presence of oxygen.[7]

Recent studies show that wheatgrass juice has a powerful ability to fight tumors without the usual toxicity of drugs that also inhibit cell-destroying agents. The many active compounds found in wheatgrass juice cleanse the blood and neutralize and digest toxins in our cells. Dr. Bernard Jensen is a renowned nutritionist who wrote *Health Magic Through Chlorophyll from Living Plant Life.* He describes several cases in which his patient's red blood cell count doubled in a matter of days, just by soaking

---

[7] Wigmore, Ann, and the Hippocrates Health Institute, Inc. (1985). *The Wheatgrass Book: How to Grow and Use Wheatgrass to Maximize Your Health and Vitality.* Avery Health Guides.

in a chlorophyll-rich bath. He says that blood builds more quickly when the person drinks the chlorophyll-rich fresh juices on a regular basis.[8]

7. Spirulina, a type of blue-green algae, is a superfood that provides a concentrated source of protein, vitamins, antioxidants, and other nutrients. This nutrient-dense food is a valuable source for preventing malnutrition. I recommend spirulina for its rich protein content. It's 50–70% protein by weight—even better than red meat, which is about 27% protein.

It also contains all the essential amino acids, and 10 of the 12 non-essential amino acids. In all, it has 18 complex amino acids, along with a potent array of other beneficial nutrients, including B vitamins (and exceptionally high B-12), Vitamin K, calcium, iron, magnesium, selenium, manganese, potassium, zinc, and iodine.

8. Chlorella is a saltwater blue-green algae native to Taiwan and Japan. It is similar to spirulina. It has a great ability to help you detox from heavy metals, and it can help boost your energy.

Chlorella's rich green color comes from a high concentration of chlorophyll, which helps oxygenate cells. Antioxidants are the color pigment and this food has vibrant color. Like spirulina, chlorella is nutrient-

---

[8] Jensen, Dr. Bernard. (1973). *Health Magic Through Chlorophyll from Living Plant Life.* Jensen's Health and Nutrition.

dense. For example, one ounce (3 T.) of chlorella has 16 grams of protein, 287% RDA (Required Daily Amount) of Vitamin A, 71% RDA of Vitamin B2, 33% RDA of Vitamin B3, 202% RDA of Iron, 22% RDA of Magnesium, 133% RDA of Zinc.

In addition, chlorella contains a good amount of Vitamin B1, Vitamin B6, vitamin C, Vitamin E, folate, calcium, magnesium, copper and phosphorus. It is a *powerhouse* of nutrition with more nutrients per gram than other green foods such as kale, spinach, and broccoli!

9. Coconut oil, a type of "nut" fat, is highly effective as an antioxidant. In most parts of the world, it is seen as the superfood of fats. It is a unique saturated fat and a medium-chain fatty acid, which means that pancreatic enzymes or bile are not required for the body to process it. This also means it is easily absorbed. Coconut oil nourishes the body, and the medium-chained fatty acids provide a good source of energy.

Also, the lauric acid in coconut oil is a natural immune system booster. [9] For years, many people thought coconut oil was bad for your health because it raised cholesterol. But actually, it provides good cholesterol (HDL).

In fact, the top nutrition advisory panel in the U.S. is planning to drop its caution about eating cholesterol-rich food. They are no longer considering

---

[9] BBC News. (2005, January 10). "Olive Oil Acid 'Cuts Cancer Risk.'"
   http://news.bbc.co.uk/2/hi/health/4154269.stm

it a "nutrient of concern." They have found that rich foods heavy with saturated animal fats are the biggest danger to people's health. Rich, fatty meats and dairy contribute to a risk of heart disease.[10]

Pure coconut oil has many benefits. Some of these include:

o Coconut oil is easy to digest.
o It has anti-microbial and anti-fungal properties.
o When coconut oil is processed by the liver, it is immediately converted into energy instead of being stored as fat.
o Coconut oil supports brain health. When the medium chain fatty acids of coconut oil are digested by the liver, it creates ketones. Ketones allow the brain to access glucose from the bloodstream without using insulin.
o Coconut oil has been shown to heal urinary (UTI) and kidney infections. The medium chain fatty acids in the oil work as a natural antibiotic. They do this by disrupting the lipid coating on bacteria and killing them.[11]

---

[10] Whoriskey, Peter. (Feb. 10, 2015). "The US government is poised to withdraw longstanding warnings about cholesterol." *The Washington Post.*
http://www.washingtonpost.com/blogs/wonkblog/wp/2015/02/10/feds-poised-to-withdraw-longstanding-warnings-about-dietary-cholesterol/
[11] Otuechere, C., et. al. (May, 2014). "Virgin coconut oil protects against liver damage in albino rats challenged with the anti-folate combination, trimethoprim-sulfamethoxazole." *J Basic Clin Physiol Pharmacol.,* (25)2: 249-53. doi: 10.1515/jbcpp-2013-0059.

○ Coconut oil can directly protect the liver from damage.[12]

Also, coconut water is extremely hydrating. It is high in electrolytes. You can use that in the tube feeding mixture as one of the liquids. Doctors have also used coconut water injections to clear up kidney stones.[13]

Using pure, high-quality coconut oil or water in the tube feeding formula will contribute to overall health and well-being.

10. Fulvic Acid is the end product of the decomposition of organic matter, which is nutrient dense. It is something like compost, but the smallest concentrated particle of compost. It's a micro-nano molecule, which means it is incredibly small and able to cross all blood-brain barriers and carry nutrients to the cells.

Its antioxidant capacity is enormous. One molecule of fulvic acid has 14 tetratrillion electrons that it can donate to help eliminate free radicals. It is an antioxidant agent that can act as an electrolyte in the cell.

Fulvic acid been used by Dr. Daniel Nuzum, DO, NMD (toxicologist, professor, scientist, and

---

[12] Ibid.

[13] Gandhi, M., et. al. (Jan–Feb., 2013). "Prophylactic effect of coconut water (Cocos nucifera L.) on ethylene glycol induced nephrocalcinosis in male wistar rat." *Int Braz J Urol.*, (39)1:108–17. doi: 10.1590/S1677-5538.IBJU.2013.01.14.

researcher) for cancer therapy. He says that fulvic acid has the "electrolyte capacity to raise the electrical capacity in the cells and it destroys cancer cells that way."[14] If it can do this, then it is an important nutrient we should all take for optimum health.

Dr. Nuzum said he has been researching fulvic acid since 1996 and has only had good results. He went on to say that he has his whole family (including his children) take it daily.[15]

It comes in a liquid with a dropper. You take it in small doses. It doesn't taste very good, so I add it to my smoothies in the morning so I don't taste it.

11. Mucuna pruriens, also known as Mucuna, is an oily seed, usually purchased in the form of a powder. Taking Macuna can directly affect the nervous system, and can strengthen any weakened areas of the body, even enhancing the intellect.[16] In fact, the seeds of Mucuna pruriens are considered a tonic specific to neurons.[17, 18]

Energizing, revitalizing, and nourishing, Mucuna is primarily sweet and bitter, and is quite warming. It

---

[14] Nuzum, Daniel. (2014). The Truth about Cancer, "The Quest for the Cure." Complete Transcripts, pp. 194-195. *Episode 9, Proven treatments protocols*. TTAC Publishing, LLC.

[15] Ibid.

[16] Pole, Sebastian. (2006). *Ayurvedic Medicine: The Principles of Traditional Practice*, p. 77, 206. Churchill Livingston Elsevier.

[17] Gogte, Vaidya V. M. (2009). *Ayurvedic Pharmacology & Therapeutic Uses of Medicinal Plants*, p. 329-30. Chaukhambha Publications.

[18] Katzenschlager R. (December, 2004). "Mucuna pruriens in Parkinson's Disease: A Double Blind Clinical and Pharmacological Study." *J Neurol Neurosurg Psychiatry*, (75)12: 1672-7.

has an affinity for all the tissues in the body, but is especially suited to balancing the nervous, reproductive, and digestive systems.[19] Mucuna can help promote healthy digestive function and promote proper elimination.[20]

There have also been studies that show it can help people with Parkinson's Disease.[21]

12. Lemons and limes are members of the same citrus family. Limes are a green fruit and smaller, whereas lemons are yellow and usually larger. Despite the difference in flavor, color, and size, limes and lemons basically have the same nutritional benefits.

Their peels contain even more nutrients, vitamins, and health benefits than the juice—as much as five to ten times more. That is why I have included the peels in my juicing recipe.

We might consider lemons acidic, but the body reads lemons as alkalizing. (Limes are slightly less alkalizing.) Diseases such as cancer thrive in an acidic environment. Consuming lemons makes the body becomes more alkaline.

Lemon and lime peels are also an excellent source of fiber, potassium, magnesium, calcium, folate, beta carotene, bioactive flavonoids, and Vitamin C. The bioactive flavonoids (phytonutrients) are a critical

---

[19] Pole.
[20] Ibid.
[21] Katzenschlager.

component for the proper absorption of the Vitamin C. Nutrients in foods work in unison like a symphony.

Studies have shown that bioactive flavonoids can increase and prolong the action of Vitamin C. Oranges and tangerines also have high levels of bioactive flavonoids, and you can use them in place of the lemon or lime in this recipe to add some variety to the tube feeding plan.

The best type of any fruit or vegetable is one that has been tree or vine-ripened. Tree or vine-ripened food have salvestrols in them, which have powerful cancer-fighting properties. Foods picked before they are ripe do not have these salvestrols in them. Tree-ripened lemons and limes contain the salvestrol Q40 and limonene, which have been shown to help prevent and treat cancer and other diseases.

Be aware that many Vitamin C supplements consist of synthetically derived ascorbic acid. Without the natural citrus bioflavonoids found in the natural fruit or juice itself, the ascorbic acid is easily oxidized and can actually be harmful to the body. This is why whole-food nutrition is so much better than synthetically derived supplements. These citrus bioflavonoids are very powerful at reducing levels of oxidative stress and also aid in eradicating toxins and carcinogens.

5
Juicing the Ingredients for Tube Feeding

A juicer is an investment, but it will give you dense nutrients that are beneficial to health. You really need to have two different types of juicers: one for the grasses, and one for large fruits and vegetables. Large juicers usually don't do grasses. Grass juicers don't handle large vegetables very well. For grasses, I think the hand-turned wheatgrass juicer is the best choice. It is less expensive and more reliable.

Juicing is great for everyone. For people who are trying to heal from various diseases, it can be especially powerful, with all of its nutrient-rich anti-oxidant enzymes! Gabriel Cousens, MD, who wrote *There Is a Cure for Diabetes*, believes in and promotes juicing. In his book, he talks about juice feasting. What I found out about juicing is that when I am drinking these fresh, nutrient-dense juices, I never feel hungry or tired.

For diabetics, the following foods have an insulin-type of action: asparagus, avocados, bitter melon, black pepper, Brussels sprouts, carrots, cinnamon, cucumbers, fennel, garlic, ginger, grapefruit, guava, parsnips, raw green vegetables, onions, leeks, sweet potatoes, tomato, winter squash, wheatgrass, sprouts, and yams.

These foods are good choices for diabetics (or anyone, really). Just pick a few and vary them with the seasons as often as you can. At the Tree of Life, where I studied raw food and organic gardening, they did not put carrots in the juices for diabetics because carrots have a high sugar content; keep this in mind if you are diabetic.

Juicer Recommendations:

Breville Juicer: This relatively low-priced juicer is easy to use and clean. The Breville Juice Fountain boasts several features that other popular juice extractor brands simply don't have. This site has good prices for the Breville Juicer.
http://www.compare99.com/search?q=Breville-Juicers

Lexen Juicers: LexenProducts.com

Discount Juicers: DiscountJuicers.com has a large selection of juicers for wheatgrass and various other fruits and vegetables which often require different juicers for juicing. Some are manual and some are electric. The site has information about the different juicers, and rates them.

6
Additional Nutrient Information

The American Dietetic Association's (ADA) position statement on vegetarian diets states that well-planned vegetarian diets are "a healthy, nutritionally adequate dietary practice for all stages of life."

The Cleveland Heart Clinic states that the more protein—especially animal protein—one eats, the higher the risk of different chronic diseases. For example, in a recent study of more than 6,000 people in the best nationally representative dietary survey in the United States, those between 50 and 65 years old who reported high protein intake had a 75% increase in dying from any cause, a four-fold increase in cancer death risk during the following 18 years, and a five-fold increase in death from diabetes. Those with moderate intake had increased cancer death risk three-fold when compared with the low protein intake group!

The **quality** of the ingredients you use is paramount to the quality and nutrient density of the food, so always choose the best, freshest ingredients you can, and opt for organic and non-GMO when possible.

Avoid sugar. One teaspoon of sugar can suppress the immune system for up to five hours, so be aware of anything you are using that has any sugar of any kind in it. Avoid using them completely.

Studies conducted by the *American Journal of Clinical Nutrition* found that diabetes and obesity are directly linked to eating refined sugar and high-fructose corn syrup—the cheapest form of sugar and the choice of many food manufacturing companies.[22]

Along with diabetes and obesity, sugar intake can contribute to hypoglycemia, cardiovascular disease, kidney disease, high blood pressure, tooth decay, systemic infections, memory disorders, allergies, upset hormonal imbalances, and autoimmune and immune deficiency disorders. It supports the growth of cancer cells.

The list of health problems goes on to include adrenal gland exhaustion, anxiety, bloating, bone loss, eczema, cataracts, candidiasis, insomnia, ulcers, psoriasis, over-acidity, gout, gallstones, fatigue, acne, menstrual difficulties, indigestion, high triglyceride levels, and more. These are all good reasons to limit the amount of sugar in one's diet—especially high-fructose corn syrup or fructose, or fructose crystals.

Fructose, particularly as high-fructose corn syrup and fructose crystals, is very hard on the body and the digestive system. These sugars are read by the body as nutrient-empty. When the body consumes them, it must pull stored nutrients out of itself to process

---

[22] Kearns, Cristin E., et. Al. (September 12, 2016). "Sugar Industry and Coronary Heart Disease Research: A Historical Analysis of Internal Industry Documents." *JAMA Internal Medicine*.

them. This depletes the body of stored nutrients and can result in extreme cravings for nutrients. That is why feeding the body empty calories of refined carbohydrates, such as white sugar, can result in hunger pangs.

I recommend completely avoiding fake sugars and sugar substitutes. Chemically-derived sweeteners can have many harmful effects on health. Artificial sweeteners are never a healthy sugar alternative. All artificial chemical sweeteners are toxic and can indirectly lead to weight gain.

They are addictive and amplify the craving for sugar, which is the opposite reason why many people consume them. In fact, given a choice between high-fructose corn syrup and artificial sweeteners, high-fructose corn syrup is recommended by far—though it's essentially asking if you should consume poison or worse poison.[23] Stick with real, whole, unrefined, and unprocessed sugars.

Chromium is a mineral that helps transport glucose from the blood to the muscles. According to the National Institutes of Health, "Chromium is known to enhance the action of insulin, a hormone critical to the metabolism and storage of carbohydrates, fat, and

---

[23] Goulart, Frances Sheridan. (1991, March 1). "Are You Sugar Smart? Linked to Heart Attacks, Kidney Disease, Diabetes and Other Diseases, Sugar Is to the 90s What Cholesterol Was to the '80s (Includes 9 ways to Cope with Sugar Cravings)." *American Fitness.* http://www.highbeam.com/doc/1G1-10722552.html

protein in the body."[24]

People who eat non-organic foods have a greater likelihood of being deficient in this important trace mineral. The chemical fertilizers used in industrial farming destroy the chromium that would naturally be in the soil. This is one of many reasons organic food is always the best choice at the grocery store.

Chromium supplements should have GTF (Glucose Tolerance Factor) on the label. It should say, "Chromium GTF". Avoid synthetic supplements that don't list whole, organic foods as the ingredients. (I purchase the brand "Innate" from 7 Lights.)

Cinnamon is emerging as a true wonder food. Cinnamon is a spice, and it's obtained from the inner bark of a few tree species. Research shows that cinnamon can help lower blood sugar, cholesterol, and triglyceride levels in people with Type 2 diabetes. Cinnamon contains antioxidants that create healthier arteries and reduce the risk of cardiovascular disease. Cinnamon can also benefit us with increased alertness and energized senses. Even a teaspoon a day helps tame blood sugar levels.

Ceylon cinnamon is the best cinnamon to use. Cassia, Saigon, and Chinese cinnamon contain up to 5% coumarin, which is problematic for the liver. Ceylon cinnamon has only .004% coumarin. Sprinkle

---

[24] National Institutes of Health, Office of Dietary Supplements. "Chromium: Dietary Supplement Fact Sheet." http://ods.od.nih.gov/factsheets/Chromium-HealthProfessional/#h10

it on your morning toast, oatmeal, or other dishes. Ceylon cinnamon has many health benefits for you. It:

- significantly reduces blood sugar levels, triglycerides, and LDL (bad) cholesterol in people with Type 2 diabetes.
- improves the effectiveness, or sensitivity, of insulin.
- supports the digestive function.
- relieves congestion.
- relieves pain and stiffness of muscles and joints.
- contains anti-inflammatory compounds that relieve arthritis.
- helps prevent urinary tract infections, tooth decay, and gum disease.
- relieves menstrual discomfort.
- contains blood-thinning compounds that stimulate circulation.

Enzymes are necessary for digestion and nutrient absorption. Live enzymes in foods help us digest efficiently and completely. The key to health is a clean and nutrient-rich body. Raw and living foods are the best form of foods for optimum health and wellness. These foods will feed the body on a deep, cellular level without stressing it as much as cooked food does. Cooked foods are dead. They don't supply any live enzymes.

When foods are devoid of living enzymes, it means the body must work much harder and supply more of its own enzyme store to digest the foods. Pulling enzymes from storage and using them to digest enzyme-empty food makes the body work harder, compared to eating foods that supply their own enzymes ready for digestion.

Magnesium is a trace mineral necessary for hundreds of bodily functions. Magnesium deficiency has been linked to diabetes, migraines, allergies, anxiety, asthma, attention deficit disorder, calcification of soft tissue (including the heart valve), muscle cramps, osteoporosis, fibromyalgia, hearing loss, menstrual cramps, insomnia, irritability, trembling, twitching, and more. Magnesium deficiency can cause increased levels of adrenaline, which can cause feelings of anxiety.

A Brown University study found magnesium extremely beneficial for children with acute asthma. Additionally, children with sensitive hearing may have low magnesium levels. Two separate research teams comprised of researchers at the Harvard School of Public Health and Harvard Medical School found a link between magnesium and reduced Type 2 diabetes risk, findings published in the January, 2004 issue of the journal *Diabetes Care.*

Yet 56% of Americans do not get enough magnesium from their diet.[25] Another reason so many people are deficient in magnesium may be the use of calcium supplements that don't include magnesium.

---

[25] http://www.ars.usda.gov/northeast-area/beltsville-md/beltsville-human-nutrition-research-center/docs/magnesium/

"High calcium intakes can make magnesium deficiency worse," according to Forrest Nielsen. He says consuming additional magnesium can help. In an article on the USDA Agriculture Research Service website, Mr. Nielsen goes on to say: "The diets of many people do not contain enough magnesium for good health and sleep."[26]

Foods containing magnesium are whole grains, nuts, and vegetables, especially green, leafy vegetables. Beans contain magnesium, too—even cacao, which is where chocolate comes from. Cacao is a little bitter, which is why chocolatiers add sugar. But in its raw, unsweetened form, it is actually very healthy!

Some tasty magnesium-rich food choices for children are baked potatoes, bananas, coconut milk, peas, peanut butter, bean burritos, cacao, and cashews. Caffeine and alcohol can cause a magnesium loss. Foods and drinks that are high in caffeine include: coffee, tea, some energy drinks and bars, and various types of soda.

An easy way to add magnesium to your body is to take an Epsom salt bath. Epsom salt baths can help prevent a magnesium deficiency. Epsom salts are formed from a pure mineral compound containing magnesium and sulfate. Both magnesium and sulfate stimulate detoxification in the body. Magnesium and sulfate are both minerals that can be absorbed

---

[26] Nielsen, Forrest. "Do You Have Trouble Sleeping? More Magnesium Might Help." *USDA's Agricultural Research Service.*

through our skin and taken up into the bloodstream in a bath.

So, at the end of the day, when you are ready for bed, take an Epsom salt bath, relax, and supplement your body's magnesium levels. It helps you sleep better and helps your health in so many ways.

Mushrooms. According to a study conducted by The University of Western Australia in Perth, eating mushrooms daily may reduce breast cancer risk by nearly two thirds. The study, conducted in China, looked at more than 2000 women, half of whom had suffered from breast cancer. Researchers found the women who ate a third of an ounce of fresh mushrooms every day had lowered their risk of developing a tumor by 64%.

Dried mushrooms didn't have quite the same benefit, but still reduced the risk "by around half." The study also found that the women who regularly drank green tea, combined with their daily serving of fresh mushrooms, reduced their risk by 90%.

When reporting this study in 2009, *The Telegraph* went on to say that animal tests show mushrooms have "anti-tumor properties and can stimulate the immune system's defenses." Mushrooms might accomplish this by blocking "the body's production of the hormone oestrogen, which can encourage the development of cancer."[27]

---

[27] "Eating mushrooms daily 'may cut breast cancer risk by two thirds'." (March 16, 2009). *The Telegraph*.

As the author of *How to Be a Healthy Vegetarian*, I promote a plant-based diet. A vegetarian diet "provides a variety of cancer-protective dietary factors," according to a study published in *The American Journal of Clinical Nutrition*. A vegetarian diet reduces obesity. This study's author notes that obesity increases cancer risk, and that because the Body Mass Index (BMI) "of vegans is considerably lower than that of non-vegetarians," a plant-based diet "may be an important protective factor for lowering cancer risk." [28] Mushrooms are low in calories and are 80–90% water, which makes them a great substitute for meat when you want to cut calories.

Mushrooms have been studied extensively for their health benefits because they have been found to aid the immune system. These dense, smooth, earthy fungi grow in thousands of varieties, and most of them are rich in potassium, selenium, copper, riboflavin, niacin, pantothenic acid, and B-complex vitamins. One medium Portobello mushroom has more potassium than a small banana. Five medium cremini mushrooms have more selenium than a large egg or three ounces of lean beef.

Plus, the copper in mushrooms helps you make red blood cells, which carry oxygen throughout your

---

http://www.telegraph.co.uk/news/health/news/5000582/Eating-mushrooms-daily-may-cut-breast-cancer-risk-by-two-thirds.html

[28] Craig, Winston J. (March 11, 2009). "Health effects of vegan diets." *The American Journal of Clinical Nutrition*, 89(supplement): 1627S-1633S. http://ajcn.nutrition.org/content/89/5/1627S.full.pdf

body. Mushrooms are an excellent source of the antioxidants known as polyphenols, selenium, and ergothioneine. Ergothioneine is a master antioxidant, an amino acid containing sulfur. Sulfur is an extremely important nutrient, yet it is often overlooked.

There are many varieties of mushrooms, thousands of which are poisonous, so do *not* pick them in the wild. Always buy them from a reliable and reputable supplier. Look for mushrooms that are smooth, clean, and fresh in appearance. To clean them, use a soft mushroom brush or wet paper towel to remove any parts that look dirty or mushy. You can rinse them, but do not soak them.

Keep them refrigerated in the original container until you're ready to use them. They can keep up to a week in the refrigerator in a porous paper bag, but never put mushrooms in an airtight container and never freeze them. Always trim the end of the stem before you use mushrooms. If the stems are too tough, just use the caps.

Adding mushrooms to dishes is easy. Thinly slice them for salads, pasta dishes, and sandwiches—or serve them as a side dish. Grilling them is always great, and mushrooms make a tasty and healthy alternative to a burger. I love to sauté them with onions and butter to bring out the rich flavor of savory mushrooms. Each mushroom has a different flavor, so experiment by trying different varieties.

Reishi mushrooms, the "Mushrooms of

Immortality", have been used to treat countless ailments in the Far East for over 2,000 years because of their extraordinary medicinal properties.

They have been found to decrease inflammation, increase energy levels, repair damaged blood vessels, and relieve hormonal imbalances. Studies have repeatedly shown that reishi mushrooms have antioxidant abilities that strengthen the body's defenses against cancer, diabetes, autoimmune diseases, heart disease, allergies, and infections.[29]

A study conducted by the Department of Pharmacology of Peking University in Beijing and published December, 2006 in the *Journal of Asian Natural Products Research* looked into the reishi mushroom's effects on diabetic kidney disease. After the eight-week trial period, the diabetic subjects showed noticeable reduction of markers in kidney stress, and a considerable reduction of triglyceride and blood sugar levels. The researchers concluded that reishi mushrooms could prevent or halt the progression of diabetic kidney complications.[30]

The mushroom is tough and woody, so you need it in a powder or extract when using it as a supplement. The reishi mushroom supplement is effective in reducing blood sugar levels, and the amounts of insulin required for diabetic patients. For non-insulin dependent patients, it is possible to have a better

---

[29] Ibid.
[30] Seto, S.W. (May, 2009). "Novel hypoglycemic effects of Ganoderma lucidum water-extract in obese/diabetic (+db/+db) mice." *Phytomedicine, 16*(5): 426-36. doi: 10.1016/j.phymed.2008.10.004

result. Diabetics should see significant effects within 1 or 2 months. The usual dose recommended is 3 or 4 capsules, 3 times daily.[31]

Chaga mushrooms are an adaptogen.

Adaptogen mushrooms help to bring the body back into balance and have beneficial effects on the nervous system, immune system, the GI tract, the cardiovascular system, and the endocrine system. By supporting the body and mind in these ways, adaptogens help us to cope with stress, stay healthy during the cold and flu season, fight cancer, and lift us out of the dark depths of depression and adrenal burnout. They have immune-modulating properties that make them helpful in treating auto-immune diseases and have high levels of anti-oxidants that protect cells from damaging free radicals.[32]

You can use mushroom extract in the formula for tube feeding and it will be thin and easy to combine.

Omega 3 fatty acids are healthy fats our bodies cannot make and must obtain from food. Studies show that adding Omega 3 fatty acids to your diet

---

[31] Lo, H.C, and Wasser, S.P. (2011). "Medicinal mushrooms for glycemic control in diabetes mellitus: history, current status, future perspectives, and unsolved problems (review)." *Int J Med Mushrooms*, 13(5): 401-26.

[32] Raeven, Susanna. (January 20, 2015). "How Chaga Mushroom Can Help You Be Healthy". *Mother Earth News*.
http://www.motherearthnews.com/natural-health/chaga-mushroom-can-help-you-to-be-healthy-zbcz1501

promotes healthy blood sugar levels. Try adding cold-pressed, organic flax or hemp seed oil to your smoothies and other foods, like oatmeal chia seed pudding in the morning.

Probiotics and Our Immune System. More than 70% of our immune system is located in our digestive tract in the form of micro flora, or beneficial bacteria, which we now call **probiotics**. *Pr*obiotics are mostly bacteria, which assist in the maintenance of the natural balance of microorganisms (micro flora) in the intestines. A normal, healthy human digestive tract has approximately 400 types of probiotic bacteria.

Friendly bacteria (micro flora) are paramount to the proper development of the immune system, for protection against microorganisms that can cause disease, and for the digestion and absorption of food and nutrients.

By contrast, unhealthy or imbalanced intestinal microorganisms (micro flora) are implicated in chronic diseases such as heart disease, some cancers, allergies, asthma, obesity, IBS, and digestive problems.

When we are healthy, it largely because these probiotics (beneficial bacteria) are healthy. The probiotics help us digest and absorb our food, boost our immune systems, and even contribute to the manufacturing of certain vitamins that are necessary for our overall health and well-being.

Protein. The number one thing I always get asked about is protein. Protein is essential to our diets, but many people think you can only get it from eating meats or, as I call them, creature foods.

The fact is, plant-based proteins are much more easily used by the body and are just as effective.

Protein is made up of amino acids, which are crucial for building and maintaining all your cells and tissues. Your body also uses amino acids to make hemoglobin and insulin. Protein is absolutely essential for maintaining healthy sugar levels in the blood, especially when eating carbohydrates.

Many people don't realize that plants such as broccoli have, calorie-for-calorie, two times as much protein as steak, and are much easier for the body to digest than the animal protein.

Besides plants, here are several other ways to add protein to your meals. For an optimum protein source from a supplement, use a nutrient-dense mixture such as the Garden of Life Protein Supplement. Garden of Life has a variety of protein mixtures to choose from. They are all gluten-free, GMO-free, raw, and organic. They also contain a variety of plant-based proteins that are sprouted, which makes them easier to digest.

Always avoid soy and soy products. I know soy and soy milk are advertised as health foods, but that is incorrect. Soy and soy milk are not healthy foods. Soy and soy products are extremely hard on the body and very difficult to digest. Soy can also prevent the body from absorbing important nutrients, and its goitrogens can harm the thyroid.

The thyroid gland is one of the largest in the endocrine system. It is in the neck, below some cartilage. The thyroid controls how your body responds to other hormones, helps makes certain proteins, and controls energy levels. I never recommend soy to any of my clients or my family. I never use it, unless the soy is certified organic, non-GMO, sprouted, and fermented (all four of those).

For a protein-packed "creature food" that is not plant based, I recommend eggs—but only if you have access to healthy chickens that are living a healthy life with fresh air, sunshine, exercise, and a natural, happy environment. If that is the case, then I suggest adding a fresh, organic egg to your recipe.

Eggs can be controversial. But, "a 2011 study in the journal *Food Chemistry* found that regular egg consumption may be associated with a reduced risk of cardiovascular disease and cancer because of their high levels of antioxidants."[33]

I suggest eggs because, when I was in health and nutrition school, I had at least three separate and well-renowned doctors recommend that the yolk of an egg is one of the healthiest foods available. "Eggs are a complete food."[34]

Egg yolks can have Vitamins A, D, E, and K. In fact,

---

[33] Nimalarante, C., et. al. (November 2011). "Free aromatic amino acids in egg yolk show antioxidant properties". *Food Chemistry*, (129)1: 155–161.

[34] Washington University in St. Louis. (June 7, 2017). "Eggs can significantly increase growth in young children." *EurekaAlert!* http://www.eurekalert.org/pub_releases/2017-06/wuis-ecs052517.php

the egg yolk is one of the few foods that contains Vitamin D. Eggs also have nutrients such as lutein and zeaxanthin, which are carotenoids that may be beneficial in lowering the risk of macular degeneration. Eggs also contain choline, which may be good for memory. The yolk also contains calcium, copper, iron, manganese, phosphorus, selenium and zinc.

I use whole, raw eggs in my smoothies when I have a high-quality, fresh, organic, humanely and pasture-raised egg.

When I was a child, my father would make us smoothies in the morning, and he would add raw eggs that our pet chickens would lay in our back yard. The smoothies were delicious. Dad called them "milk punch", because he would use milk in the mixture.

Now I use an alternative milk, like unsweetened coconut milk. But those smoothies Dad made us were packed with protein and many other healthy nutrients because of the fresh eggs he used as ingredients.

The yolk and egg white also have a good amount of a certain type of protein the liver needs to make albumin. The liver is responsible for filtering proteins in the blood and breaking the proteins down into smaller molecules for use. The liver uses these proteins to create albumin, which is then circulated throughout the body. We need to have 3.4 and 5.4 g/dL of albumin in the blood to maintain normal levels. The albumin helps create the fluid balance in the body.

Albumin is the most abundant protein in the blood other than the proteins making up all the cells.

Our cells are a lot like balloons, because they can lose oxygen or fluid and require a refill. The cell walls can be fragile and can burst, like a balloon. If a person is low in albumin, the fluids will leak into other parts of the body and create swelling.

If you take medications such as anabolic steroids, androgen hormones, growth hormones, or insulin, you might experience an increase in albumin levels. This can result in dehydration and your cells' starting to take in more water in an attempt to balance the high amounts of albumin.

Malnutrition (especially protein malnutrition), liver and kidney disease, smoking, decreased muscle mass, and low amounts of physical exercise can all result in lower albumin levels. Liver and kidney disease can affect your body's ability to use proteins properly, and swelling and inflammation can occur.

Have your levels of albumin and protein checked regularly to make sure you have the optimum amount.

In addition to the albumin, eggs added to the diet have been shown to significantly increase growth and reduce stunting by 47% in young children. This fidning comes from a new study by a leading expert on child nutrition at the Brown School at Washington University in St. Louis.[35]

---

[35] Ibid.

Sea Salt. Unrefined sea salt promotes the proper balance for the endocrine, adrenal, and thyroid glands to function properly. It supports healthy blood pressure, detoxifies the body, and—along with water—is necessary for the optimal functioning of the immune system, hormonal system, and cardiovascular health.

Dr. David Brownstein says low-salt diets "promote toxicity" and have "adverse effects on numerous metabolic markers, including promoting elevated insulin levels and insulin resistance. Low- salt diets have been associated with elevating normal cholesterol and LDL cholesterol levels, which in turn, have been associated with cardiovascular disease. Finally, low-salt diets will lead to mineral deficiencies and the development of chronic disease."[36]

Sprouts and micro greens are the ultimate superfood—incredibly nutritious and packed with power. Sprouts and micro greens are the basis of life because they rejuvenate, re-energize, and heal. Sprouts and microgreens are some of the most nutritionally-rich foods. They are complete foods, they contain protein, carbohydrates, and good fat. They are rich in vitamins, minerals, and natural enzymes.

Studies have shown that when seeds and grains are germinated, they show an increase in "activities of

---

[36] Brownstein, David. (2012). *Salt Your Way to Health*. 2nd edition. Medical Alternative Press.

hydrolytic enzymes, improvement in the contents of certain essential amino acids, total sugars, and B-group vitamins, and a decrease in dry matter, starch, and anti-nutrients."[37] Sprouts and micro-greens can contain all the nutritional value of the whole plant in one little package!

Sulfur is an extremely important nutrient, yet it is highly overlooked. Because chemical fertilizers destroy the natural sulfur in the soil, non-organic foods don't contain this nutrient. People who eat non-organically grown types of foods are more likely to have an insufficient amount of sulfur in their body.

Sulfur is a major nutrient we need to get oxygen into our cells, and it is the third most prevalent element in the body. With sulfur being one of our body's main nutrients, this is absolutely critical to our health. Without the proper levels of sulfur, our bodies aren't able to build good healthy cells, and this leads to illness.

Sulfur is found in all organically grown foods. But, due to its unstable nature, sulfur is quickly lost from food when it is processed, cooked, or stored. That is why a diet high in freshly picked, raw, unprocessed, whole, organic food is so vitally important.

The powdered variety of sulfur (methylsulfonylmethane, known as MSM) has limited effectiveness as a dietary supplement. Powdering it or

---

[37] Azulay, Sol. "Sprouts in the News." *International Specialty Supply*. http://www.sproutnet.com/Sprouts-in-the-Press

combining it with magnesium stearate, which is used as a filler in many supplements, can render the sulfur in MSM fairly useless.

Dr. Johanna Budwig, a German biochemist and author, lived from 1908–2003. She worked as a pharmacist and held doctorate degrees in physics and chemistry. She researched fatty acids, and she developed a diet she thought important in the treatment of cancer She was nominated seven times for the Nobel Prize.

Dr. Budwig was considered an expert in several fields such as pharmacology, physics, and chemistry— specifically, the chemistry of fats. Dr. Budwig contributed to the Federal Research Institute of Fats and Oils. Today, her discoveries are still held in high regard.

She discovered that when she combined flax seed oil with organic cottage cheese or kefir, which contains sulfurated proteins, there was a chemical reaction which made the fat compounds water-soluble and absorbable by the cell membrane.

You can get more natural sulfur into your body by swimming, bathing, or drinking water from a natural spring or well that contains natural, organic sulfur. This type of water has been known for its healing qualities for centuries.

Turmeric is one of the most potent healing herbs on earth. It contains a compound called curcumin. Curcumin is a substance that attributes to turmeric's powerful antioxidant and anti-inflammatory properties. It has been found to help decrease chronic inflammation, boosts the immune system, help with irritable bowel syndrome, just to name a few.[38]

Turmeric has been studied extensively, but recent research has shown that curcumin dramatically decreased brain tumors by 81% in 9 out of the 11 studies examined.[39]

Turmeric can be taken in capsule form or added to recipes like curry. With a feeding tube, the spice won't be tasted when you add it to the mixture. If you combine the turmeric with black pepper and a healthy fat, it can be absorbed as much as 20 times more effectively. Some turmeric capsules may already have black pepper added to them, so always check the ingredients label.

Vitamin B Complex. Although all nutrients and minerals are important for optimum health, there are a few nutrients that are *critical* to health. One of those nutrients is the Vitamin B complex.

How much of the B vitamins do you need? It depends on your age, medical conditions, and diet. Vitamin B deficiencies can stem from weight-loss surgery, celiac disease, Crohn's disease, commonly prescribed heartburn medications, and a mainly

---

[38] Seto, S.W. (May, 2009). "Novel hypoglycemic effects of Ganoderma lucidum water-extract in obese/diabetic (+db/+db) mice." *Phytomedicine, 16*(5): 426-36. doi: 10.1016/j.phymed.2008.10.004.

[39] Soo, Teow Sun. (2004). "Effective dosage of the extract of ganoderma lucidum in the treatment of various ailments." *Mushworld.*

vegetarian or vegan diet.

I will share with you some ways you can make certain you are getting an adequate amount of all the B vitamins.

Thiamine (Vitamin B1), riboflavin (Vitamin B2), and niacin (Vitamin B3) are necessary for energy production.

Vitamin B5, or pantothenic acid, helps the body use fats and proteins in food and turn carbohydrates into blood sugar for energy. Foods that contain Vitamin B5 are whole grains, legumes, eggs, nuts, avocados, spinach, kale, broccoli, cauliflower, corn, and tomatoes.

Vitamin B6 helps your body process protein, as well as supporting the nervous system and immune system. Vitamin B6 is in avocados, bananas, and eggs.

Biotin (Vitamin B7) helps the body produce hormones and aids in converting food into energy.

Folate (Vitamin B9) is found in citrus fruits, peanuts, and some mushrooms. Along with Vitamin A, it is concentrated in green vegetables like romaine lettuce, spinach, turnip greens, mustard greens, parsley, collard greens, broccoli, cauliflower, beets, and lentils. The Centers for Disease Control and Prevention say expectant mothers need 400 mcg of folate daily before and during pregnancy to prevent birth defects in their babies' brain and spine.[40]

The synthetic form of folate is folic acid. High

---

[40] Centers for Disease Control and Prevention (CDC). "Folic Acid."
http://www.cdc.gov/ncbddd/folicacid/index.html

intakes of folic acid have been associated with higher risks of cancer, as well as masking B_{12} deficiencies. So, if you use a B-vitamin supplement, make sure it contains folate in a whole-food form of Vitamin B9. Look for 5-methyltetrahydrofolate or 5-MTHF as the folate, and avoid supplements that contain folic acid.

Vitamin B_{12}, or cobalamin, is unique in that it is almost exclusively found in animal sources such as meat, fish, dairy, and eggs. It is the B vitamin I have found to be vitally important for vegetarians in particular.

B_{12} is only made by microorganisms, primarily bacteria, which often live in water and soil. Animals get B_{12} by eating food and soil contaminated with these microorganisms. The bacteria require cobalt to produce B_{12}, which is why it is also known as cobalamin. Plant food can provide Vitamin B_{12} if it is taken from soil containing cobalt and is not cleaned, leaving the bacteria on it.

People eating a mostly plant-based diet should have their blood checked by a doctor to make certain they are getting enough B_{12} and other B vitamins, including folate. Vegans, who eat no animal products at all, should consistently eat foods fortified with Vitamin B_{12}—such as breakfast cereals—two or three times each day to get at least 3 mcg of B_{12} daily.

For example, if a fortified plant milk contains 1 mcg of Vitamin B_{12} per serving, then consuming three servings a day will provide adequate Vitamin B_{12}. Other vegans may find the use of Vitamin B_{12}

supplements more convenient and economical.

The less frequently you obtain Vitamin B12, the more you need to take, as Vitamin B12 is best absorbed in small amounts. A daily supplement of 10 mcg is required. But, the body's ability to absorb vitamin B12 from dietary supplements is limited. "For example, only about 10 mcg of a 500 mcg oral supplement is actually absorbed in healthy people."[41]

I have been using a new type of vitamin B12 called Methylcobalamin. You take it by spraying it under your tongue. This type of sprayable vitamin supplement is more absorbable. Methylcobalamin "is the most active form of B12 in the human body. It converts homocysteine into methionine, which helps protect the cardiovascular system. Methylcobalamin also offers overall protection to the nervous system. This Methylcobalamin B12 form can also cross the blood-brain barrier–without assistance–to protect brain cells. It contributes essential methyl groups, which are needed for detoxification and to start the body's biochemical reactions."[42]

Look for this type of supplement. When taking vitamins, you want to thrive, not just survive.

Symptoms of deficiency include energy loss, tingling, numbness, reduced sensitivity to pain or

[41] Carmel. R. (September, 2008). "How I treat cobalamin (vitamin B12) deficiency". *Blood, (112)*6: 2214-21. doi: 10.1182/blood-2008-03-040253. http://www.ncbi.nlm.nih.gov/pubmed/18606874

[42] Mercola, Joseph. (January 30, 2002). "Vitamin B12: Are You Getting It?" http://articles.mercola.com/sites/articles/archive/2002/01/30/vitamin-b12-part-three.aspx

pressure, blurred vision, abnormal gait, sore tongue, poor memory, confusion, hallucinations, and personality changes. Often these symptoms develop gradually over several months to a year before they are recognized as being due to a B12 deficiency, and they are usually reversible upon the administration of B12.[43]

When I read this list of symptoms, I was really surprised. Lack of Vitamin B could have been one of the contributing factors to vision problems I battled all my life. I read this, too:

> According to Optometrist Ben C. Lane of the Optical Society, there is a link between nearsightedness and chromium and calcium levels, which are lowered by sugar and protein consumption. The excessive intake of sugar and overcooked proteins exhaust the body's supplies of chromium and B vitamins. Fluid pressure in the eye, a contributing factor of nearsightedness, is regulated by the B vitamins.[44]

Make certain you are getting adequate amounts of all the B vitamins.

Vitamin D is essential because it influences your entire body. Receptors that respond to the vitamin

---

[43] Carmel, R.

[44] Group, Edward. (November 11, 2014). "Vitamin B12 Benefits: 4 Types and Their Health Benefits."

have been found in almost every type of human cell, from your brain to your bones. It is also involved in multiple repair and maintenance functions. It touches thousands of different genes. It regulates your immune system, and much, much more. Vitamin D regulates your ability to fight infections and chronic inflammation. It produces over 200 antimicrobial peptides.[45]

Vitamin D is a prohormone, which means the body converts it into an active form; in this case, calcitriol. A deficiency of calcitriol may be responsible for more than 17 cancers, diabetes, autoimmune disease, multiple sclerosis, osteoarthritis, hypertension/high blood pressure, depression, and genetic disorders, and it may increase the risk of cardiovascular disease.[46]

Rickets (bone softening) is a disease caused by Vitamin D deficiency. Sounds a lot like osteoporosis, doesn't it? If you have a bone problem, have your Vitamin D checked. Vitamin D deficiency has also been linked to cancer. Check with your physician to make certain the level of Vitamin D in your blood is optimal.

The body makes its own Vitamin D from cholesterol when skin is exposed to sunlight. Vitamin D is essential for everyone. Studies show approximately 85% of the US population is critically

---

[45] Wilson, Lawrence. (2014, October). "Vitamin D." DrWilson.
   http://www.drlwilson.com/ARTICLES/VITAMIN%20D.htm
[46] Ibid.

low in Vitamin D.[47]

It may be the use of sunscreen or working and staying indoors most of the day which prevents people from getting enough direct sunlight. **Get some sunshine!** Get out in the sun every day for at least 20 minutes without sunscreen. The more skin is exposed, the more sunlight you can absorb. During the winter months, it may be harder or even impossible to get the necessary amount of Vitamin D from the sun. Full-spectrum lighting indoors can significantly help with depression, mood, and health, but it is not a reliable source of Vitamin D.

Very few foods contain good levels of Vitamin D. Parsley, mushrooms that have been exposed to ultraviolet light, and cod liver oil have Vitamin D in them, but a supplement is still needed.

Recently, UC San Diego and Creighton University researched Vitamin D extensively and concluded that the recommended intake needs to be addressed. Researchers are challenging the intake of Vitamin D recommended by the National Academy of Sciences Institute of Medicine saying their Recommended Dietary Allowance for Vitamin D underestimates the need by a factor of ten. They argue that a miscalculation led to low recommendations for Vitamin D.

Robert Heaney, MD, of Creighton University wrote: "We call for the NAS-IOM and all public health authorities concerned with transmitting accurate

---

[47] Ibid.

nutritional information to the public to designate, as the RDA, a value of approximately 7,000 IU/day from all sources."[48]

I get a good deal of sunlight every day, and I live in Texas, so I thought I had an optimum level of Vitamin D in my body. I had my doctor test me, only to find out I was on the low end of optimum. This was even during the summer, so I was quite surprised! Since then, I have been taking about 5,000–6,000 IU's of Vitamin D a day—and I'm 61, and I feel great. But given the new study by Creighton, I am going to increase it to 7,000 a day.

I prefer to take supplements that are created with organic, whole-food ingredients. I avoid synthetic varieties, because research has shown that some synthetic varieties of vitamins may increase chances of cancer. I've been using vitamins that you spray under your tongue for maximum absorption. These vitamins are organic, whole food, raw and non-GMO.

In conclusion, keep an eye on your Vitamin D, and remember that as we age, we need more of it.

Zinc is one of the most important minerals used by the body. It helps with the production of approximately 100 enzymes. Zinc contributes to building up the immune system. Zinc is required for protein and DNA synthesis, insulin activity, and liver

---

[48] Science Daily. (March 17, 2015). "Recommendation for vitamin D intake was miscalculated, is far too low, experts say." *Creighton University*. http://www.sciencedaily.com/releases/2015/03/150317122458.htm

function.

Zinc is not really stored in our bodies, so we need a regular supply. Men need about one-third more zinc than women, because the prostate gland and semen are highly concentrated with zinc. A zinc deficiency may appear as skin problems, impairment of taste, a poor immune system, hair loss, diarrhea, fatigue, wounds not healing properly, or a poor or slow growth rate for infants.

Even if you eat zinc-rich foods, you may need a supplement, because phytic acid and dietary fiber in certain foods can inhibit the absorption of zinc. If you take a vitamin supplement of any kind (such as a multi-vitamin, Vitamin D, chromium, or zinc), make sure it is in a natural form, not a synthetic one. Synthetic forms of any nutrient can be harmful to the body. Instead, buy dietary supplements that show whole, organic foods in their ingredient list.

Acknowledgments

To Larry Hagman and John Castonia, I give my sincere, heartfelt thanks for your friendship and encouragement! It was wonderful working with you.

A warm thank you to Linda Gray. You have been an incredible friend ever since we met. Thank you for your friendship, support, encouragement, and belief in me.

Thank you to my wonderful family and especially my mother, Junia Gibbons, and my children, Amanda and Gibbons Addison. I am so thankful for all your support, generosity, and kindness in my life's journey. You are an amazing family, and I am blessed to be a part of it.

A special thank you to Dr. Gary Massad. Thank you so much for working with me and sharing your knowledge and expertise with me. I am very grateful for your time, effort, faith, generosity, and support. Please know how greatly it is appreciated.

To all the wonderful friends and neighbors from my life who have honored me with your friendship, endless patience, cheerful words of encouragement, and constant support, I thank you all for making my life so much brighter. Bless you all.

Thank you to my dear friend Susan Doyle for your valuable editing suggestions and assistance in so many things. I am extremely grateful and thankful to have you and Joe in my life.

Thank you so much Kaaydah Schatten and Deanna Sweet for your continued encouragement, support and input. I'm very thankful and appreciate it so very much.

Thank you, Kytka Hilmar-Jezek, for creating my cover and helping with my launch of the pamphlet. You have become a dear friend and I am thankful for you and your expertise.

Thank you, Matthew Howard, for helping me edit my book. I am very grateful for all your outstanding hard work and dedication to this project and all my projects. Your insightful suggestions and wise directives are so greatly appreciated. It is an honor to work with you and to know you.

I am grateful for all of you. Bless you all. Please accept my deepest heartfelt thanks.

I thank God for the constant love, support, inspiration, knowledge, experiences, and energy that it took to put this book together.

May God bless this book and all who read it.

Manufactured by Amazon.ca
Bolton, ON

27851777R00037